DISNEY PRINCESS

Jasmine

The Daring Princess

studio fun
INTERNATIONAL

In the city of Agrabah, a beautiful princess named
Jasmine lived in a palace with her father, the Sultan.
The law said she must marry by her next birthday.
But she didn't want to do that! She wanted to
marry for love.

Jasmine decided to run away. She put on a plain dress over her royal outfit and used a shawl to hide her crown. The thought of leaving was scary, but she knew she had no choice.

"I'm sorry, Rajah," she told her pet tiger. "But I can't stay here and have my life lived for me." She hugged him goodbye.

Disk 3

In the marketplace, Jasmine saw a hungry little boy and gave him an apple. She didn't know she was supposed to pay for it. The apple merchant grabbed her hand and called her a thief.

Suddenly, a street rat named Aladdin appeared and helped Jasmine get away. He told the guard Jasmine was his sister who got lost.

Meanwhile, the sultan's vizier, Jafar, performed a magic spell to find out who could enter the Cave of Wonders. The sand showed him that the Diamond in the Rough was Aladdin! Jafar ordered his guards to bring Aladdin to him.

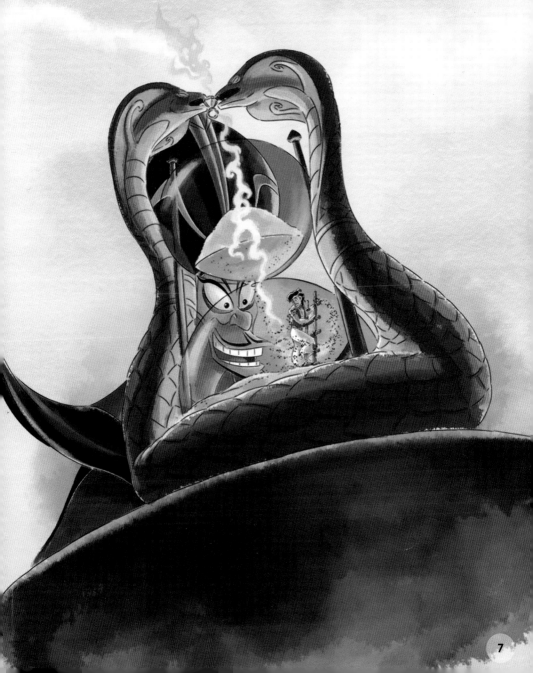

Soon the guards found Aladdin and Jasmine together. Jasmine revealed she was the princess, but the guards still took her new friend away. Angry with Jafar, Jasmine decided that when she was queen, she would get rid of him.

Aladdin was locked up in the royal dungeon. Jafar, disguised as an old man, offered to help Aladdin escape if he would retrieve the magic lamp from the Cave of Wonders.

Aladdin agreed and traveled through the desert with Jafar.

When Aladdin and his monkey, Abu, entered
the Cave, they saw more riches than they had ever
imagined. They even found a magic carpet that wanted
to be their friend, as they searched for the lamp.

Just when Aladdin found the lamp, Abu grabbed a giant jewel. The cave started falling down around them!

With the carpet's help, they barely made it back to the entrance.

3

Aladdin threw the old man the lamp, but Jafar betrayed him. The cave collapsed with Aladdin, Abu, and the carpet still inside. They were trapped, but Abu had managed to steal back the lamp!

When Aladdin rubbed the side of the lamp, a magical genie appeared! The Genie said he would grant Aladdin three wishes. The Genie got Aladdin and Abu out of the Cave. Then Aladdin asked, "What would you wish for?"

"Freedom," the Genie said. The only way that could happen was if someone wished it for him. Aladdin promised to free the Genie with his last wish.

Aladdin's first official wish was for the
Genie to make him a prince named Ali.

Then he could try to win Jasmine's heart!
Except Jasmine was not impressed.

Later that night, Prince Ali took Jasmine on a magic carpet ride all over the world! Jasmine realized that Prince Ali was actually Aladdin, the boy from the marketplace. She thought he must have gone out in public wearing regular clothes just like she had! She knew she wanted to marry him.

But Jafar wanted to marry Jasmine so he could become sultan. He tried to get rid of Aladdin for good, but it didn't work. Aladdin told everyone all the bad things Jafar had done. But Jafar escaped before anything could happen to him.

With Jafar gone, Jasmine was so happy! She could marry the person she loved.

Disk 4

Aladdin realized he needed the Genie in order to stay a prince. He told the Genie he couldn't free him after all.

Meanwhile, Jafar's parrot, Iago, stole the lamp. Now the Genie had to grant Jafar's wishes! Jafar wanted to be the most powerful sorcerer in the world!

Jafar revealed the truth about Aladdin to Jasmine and her father. He wasn't a prince. He was just a street rat! Then Jafar sent Aladdin far away and held the royals captive.

2

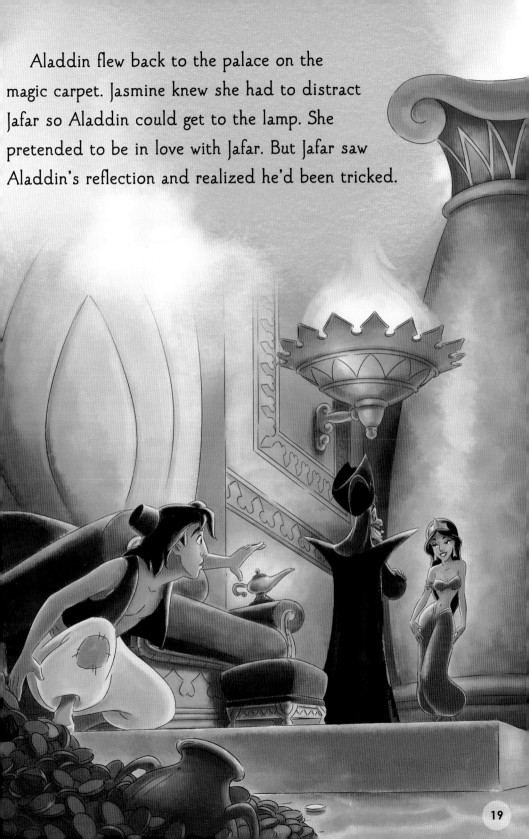

Aladdin flew back to the palace on the
magic carpet. Jasmine knew she had to distract
Jafar so Aladdin could get to the lamp. She
pretended to be in love with Jafar. But Jafar saw
Aladdin's reflection and realized he'd been tricked.

He trapped Jasmine in a giant hourglass and turned into an enormous snake.

3

Aladdin convinced Jafar into wishing to become an all-powerful genie. But Jafar forgot that he would be trapped in a lamp forever.

Then Aladdin freed Genie as promised, even though it meant he couldn't be a prince anymore. He had to stop pretending to be someone he wasn't.

As thanks to Aladdin and Jasmine for saving the palace, the Sultan changed the law so Jasmine could marry anyone she wanted! Jasmine chose Aladdin.

Together, they looked forward to a whole new world of love and happiness.